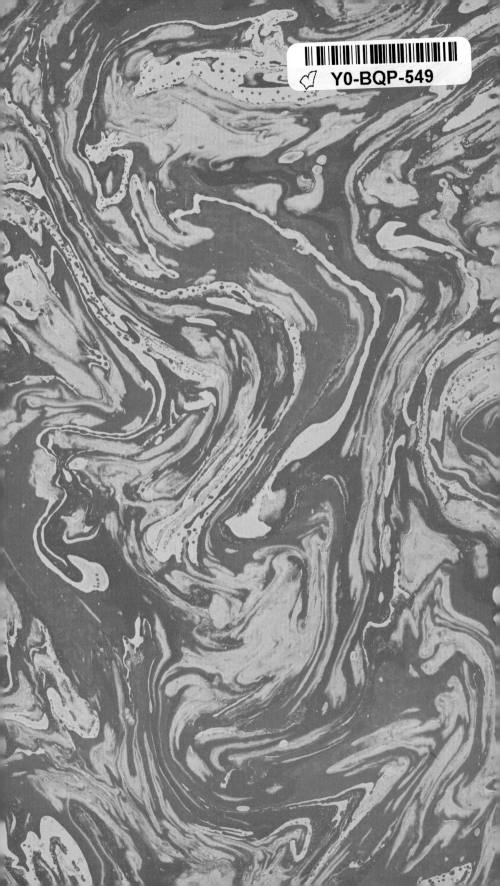

THIS LIMITED EDITION

IS PUBLISHED BY

WEST VIRGINIA PULP AND PAPER COMPANY

CHRISTMAS

1959

Mark Twain

THE

FOREWORD

Samuel Langhorne Clemens, whose pseudonym
Mark Twain instantly identifies America's
most beloved and renowned author, first won
literary acclaim with his story of the jumping frog.
The birth of that story itself has a history.

Although Twain heard and noted the incident
when he was a miner at Angel's Camp in 1849,
eighteen years were to elapse before it was published
under his name. As "A Toad Story" it had been
reported briefly in the Sonora *Herald* in 1853
and the San Andreas *Independent* printed it in 1858,
but it was not until 1865, at the suggestion
of Artemus Ward, that Twain wrote his own
first version of it.

Ward, who wished to lengthen a book—already
prepared for publication but too short for its
agreed price—asked Twain to write out and send
the jumping frog story to New York, so
that it could be added to this book as padding.

The publisher, Carleton, duly received the
manuscript, but on account of the extra expense

v

involved was unwilling to carry out Ward's
proposal, so he presented the story to Henry Clapp,
the owner of *The Saturday Press*. Entitled
"Jim Smiley and His Frog," it appeared in the
very last issue of that expiring literary
journal, and was copied therefrom by American
and English papers.

Twain related these events to publisher Charles
Henry Webb, who, recognizing the story's
merit, decided to publish "The Jumping Frog"
and some of Twain's sketches from *The
Territorial Enterprise* and other California papers.
Taking the name John Paul as a pseudonym,
Webb compiled, edited and produced
"The Celebrated Jumping Frog of Calaveras
County and Other Sketches" as a little book
in 1867. An immediate success, the book
was reprinted several times that year and heralded
Twain's metamorphosis from newspaperman
to literary figure.

Twain subsequently rewrote the jumping frog
story in several forms and with variations,
but it is from Webb's edition that we have taken the
following version and some of the sketches.
We present them in appreciation of Twain's brilliant
reflection of that young robust frontier spirit;
that love of uproarious and macabre humor,
extravagant comedy, idiom, drawl and dialect which
characterizes mid-nineteenth century America.

THE

CELEBRATED JUMPING FROG

OF CALAVERAS COUNTY

AND OTHER SKETCHES

1867

THE

CELEBRATED JUMPING FROG

OF CALAVERAS COUNTY

AND OTHER SKETCHES

By Mark Twain

TO

JOHN SMITH

whom I have known in divers and sundry
places about the world,
and whose many and manifold virtues
did always command
my esteem, I

Dedicate this Book

It is said that
the man to whom a volume is dedicated,
always buys a copy.
If this prove true in the present instance,
a princely affluence is about
to burst upon

THE AUTHOR

CONTENTS

THE

CELEBRATED JUMPING FROG

OF CALAVERAS COUNTY

Mark Twain

THE

CELEBRATED JUMPING FROG

OF CALAVERAS COUNTY

In compliance with the request of a friend of mine,
who wrote me from the East, I called on good-
natured garrulous old Simon Wheeler, and inquired
after my friend's friend, *Leonidas W.* Smiley,
as requested to do, and I hereunto append the result.
I have a lurking suspicion that *Leonidas W.* Smiley
is a myth; that my friend never knew such a
personage; and that he only conjectured that, if I
asked old Wheeler about him, it would remind
him of his infamous *Jim* Smiley, and he would go

to work and bore me nearly to death with some
infernal reminiscence of him as long and tedious as
it should be useless to me. If that was the design,
it certainly succeeded.

I found Simon Wheeler dozing comfortably by
the bar-room stove of the old, dilapidated tavern in
the ancient mining camp of Angel's, and I noticed
that he was fat and bald-headed, and had an
expression of winning gentleness and simplicity upon
his tranquil countenance. He roused up and gave me
good-day. I told him a friend of mine had
commissioned me to make some inquiries about a
cherished companion of his boyhood named
Leonidas W. Smiley — *Rev. Leonidas W.* Smiley —
a young minister of the Gospel, who he had heard
was at one time a resident of Angel's Camp.
I added that, if Mr. Wheeler could tell me any
thing about this Rev. Leonidas W. Smiley, I would
feel under many obligations to him.

Simon Wheeler backed me into a corner and
blockaded me there with his chair, and then sat me
down and reeled off the monotonous narrative which
follows this paragraph. He never smiled, he never
frowned, he never changed his voice from the
gentle-flowing key to which he tuned the initial
sentence, he never betrayed the slightest suspicion of
enthusiasm; but all through the interminable

narrative there ran a vein of impressive earnestness
and sincerity, which showed me plainly that, so far
from his imagining that there was any thing
ridiculous or funny about his story, he regarded it as
a really important matter, and admired its two
heroes as men of transcendent genius in *finesse*. To
me, the spectacle of a man drifting serenely along
through such a queer yarn without ever smiling, was
exquisitely absurd. As I said before, I asked him to
tell me what he knew of Rev. Leonidas W. Smiley,
and he replied as follows. I let him go on in his own
way, and never interrupted him once:

There was a feller here once by the name of *Jim*
Smiley, in the winter of '49 — or may be it was the
spring of '50 — I don't recollect exactly, somehow,
though what makes me think it was one or the other
is because I remember the big flume wasn't finished
when he first came to the camp; but any way, he
was the curiosest man about always betting on any
thing that turned up you ever see, if he could get
any body to bet on the other side; and if he
couldn't, he'd change sides. Any way that suited
the other man would suit him — any way just so's
he got a bet, *he* was satisfied. But still he was lucky,
uncommon lucky; he most always come out winner.
He was always ready and laying for a chance; there

couldn't be no solitry thing mentioned but that
feller'd offer to bet on it, and take any side you
please, as I was just telling you. If there was a
horse-race, you'd find him flush, or you'd find him
busted at the end of it; if there was a dog-fight, he'd
bet on it; if there was a cat-fight, he'd bet on it; if
there was a chicken-fight, he'd bet on it; why, if
there was two birds setting on a fence, he would
bet you which one would fly first; or if there was a
camp-meeting, he would be there reg'lar, to bet on
Parson Walker, which he judged to be the best
exhorter about here, and so he was, too, and a good
man. If he even seen a straddle-bug start to go
anywheres, he would bet you how long it would take
him to get wherever he was going to, and if you
took him up, he would foller that straddle-bug to
Mexico but what he would find out where he was
bound for and how long he was on the road. Lots of
the boys here has seen that Smiley, and can tell you
about him. Why, it never made no difference to
him — he would bet on *any* thing — the dangdest
feller. Parson Walker's wife laid very sick once, for
a good while, and it seemed as if they warn't going
to save her; but one morning he come in, and Smiley
asked how she was, and he said she was considerable
better — thank the Lord for his inf'nit mercy —
and coming on so smart that, with the blessing of

Prov'dence, she'd get well yet; and Smiley, before
he thought, says, "Well, I'll risk two-and-a-half
that she don't, any way."

Thish-yer Smiley had a mare—the boys called her
the fifteen-minute nag, but that was only in fun,
you know, because, of course, she was faster than
that—and he used to win money on that horse, for
all she was so slow and always had the asthma, or
the distemper, or the consumption, or something of
that kind. They used to give her two or three
hundred yards start, and then pass her under way;
but always at the fag-end of the race she'd get
excited and desperate-like, and come cavorting and
straddling up, and scattering her legs around
limber, sometimes in the air, and sometimes out to
one side amongst the fences, and kicking up m-o-r-e
dust, and raising m-o-r-e racket with her coughing
and sneezing and blowing her nose—and always
fetch up at the stand just about a neck ahead, as
near as you could cipher it down.

And he had a little small bull pup, that to look
at him you'd think he wan't worth a cent, but to
set around and look ornery, and lay for a chance to
steal something. But as soon as money was up on
him, he was a different dog; his under-jaw'd begin
to stick out like the fo'castle of a steamboat,
and his teeth would uncover, and shine savage like

the furnaces. And a dog might tackle him, and
bully-rag him, and bite him, and throw him over
his shoulder two or three times, and Andrew
Jackson—which was the name of the pup—
Andrew Jackson would never let on but what *he*
was satisfied, and hadn't expected nothing else—
and the bets being doubled and doubled on the
other side all the time, till the money was all up;
and then all of a sudden he would grab that other
dog jest by the j'int of his hind leg and freeze
to it—not chaw, you understand, but only jest
grip and hang on till they throwed up the sponge,
if it was a year. Smiley always come out winner
on that pup, till he harnessed a dog once that
didn't have no hind legs, because they'd been
sawed off by a circular saw, and when the thing
had gone along far enough, and the money was
all up, and he come to make a snatch for his pet
holt, he saw in a minute how he'd been imposed
on, and how the other dog had him in the door,
so to speak, and he 'peared surprised, and then he
looked sorter discouraged-like, and didn't try no
more to win the fight, and so he got shucked out
bad. He give Smiley a look, as much as to say his
heart was broke, and it was *his* fault, for putting up
a dog that hadn't no hind legs for him to take holt of,
which was his main dependence in a fight, and then

8

he limped off a piece and laid down and died. It was a good pup, was that Andrew Jackson, and would have made a name for hisself if he'd lived, for the stuff was in him, and he had genius — I know it, because he hadn't had no opportunities to speak of, and it don't stand to reason that a dog could make such a fight as he could under them circumstances, if he hadn't no talent. It always makes me feel sorry when I think of that last fight of his'n, and the way it turned out.

Well, thish-yer Smiley had rat-tarriers, and chicken cocks, and tom-cats, and all them kind of things, till you couldn't rest, and you couldn't fetch nothing for him to bet on but he'd match you. He ketched a frog one day, and took him home, and said he cal'klated to edercate him; and so he never done nothing for three months but set in his back yard and learn that frog to jump. And you bet you he *did* learn him, too. He'd give him a little punch behind, and the next minute you'd see that frog whirling in the air like a doughnut — see him turn one summerset, or may be a couple, if he got a good start, and come down flat-footed and all right, like a cat. He got him up so in the matter of catching flies, and kept him in practice so constant, that he'd nail a fly every time as far as he could see him. Smiley said all a frog wanted was education, and he

could do most any thing—and I believe him. Why,
I've seen him set Dan'l Webster down here on this
floor—Dan'l Webster was the name of the frog—
and sing out, "Flies, Dan'l, flies!" and quicker'n
you could wink, he'd spring straight up, and snake a
fly off'n the counter there, and flop down on the
floor again as solid as a gob of mud, and fall to
scratching the side of his head with his hind foot as
indifferent as if he hadn't no idea he'd been doin'
any more'n any frog might do. You never see a frog
so modest and straightfor'ard as he was, for all he
was so gifted. And when it come to fair and square
jumping on a dead level, he could get over more
ground at one straddle than any animal of his breed
you ever see. Jumping on a dead level was his strong
suit, you understand; and when it come to that,
Smiley would ante up money on him as long as he
had a red. Smiley was monstrous proud of his frog,
and well he might be, for fellers that had traveled
and been everywheres, all said he laid over any
frog that ever *they* see.

Well, Smiley kept the beast in a little lattice box,
and he used to fetch him down town sometimes
and lay for a bet. One day a feller—a stranger in the
camp, he was—come across him with his box, and
says:

"What might it be that you've got in the box?"

10

And Smiley says, sorter indifferent like, "It might be a parrot, or it might be a canary, may be, but it an't—it's only just a frog."

And the feller took it, and looked at it careful, and turned it round this way and that, and says, "H'm—so 'tis. Well, what's *he* good for?"

"Well," Smiley says, easy and careless, "He's good enough for *one* thing, I should judge—he can outjump ary frog in Calaveras county."

The feller took the box again, and took another long, particular look, and give it back to Smiley, and says, very deliberate, "Well, I don't see no p'ints about that frog that's any better'n any other frog."

"May be you don't," Smiley says. "May be you understand frogs, and may be you don't understand 'em; may be you've had experience, and may be you an't only a amature, as it were. Anyways, I've got *my* opinion, and I'll risk forty dollars that he can outjump any frog in Calaveras county."

And the feller studied a minute, and then says, kinder sad like, "Well, I'm only a stranger here, and I an't got no frog; but if I had a frog, I'd bet you."

And then Smiley says, "That's all right—that's all right—if you'll hold my box a minute, I'll go and get you a frog." And so the feller took the box, and put up his forty dollars along with Smiley's, and set down to wait.

So he set there a good while thinking and thinking to hisself, and then he got the frog out and prized his mouth open and took a teaspoon and filled him full of quail shot — filled him pretty near up to his chin — and set him on the floor. Smiley he went to the swamp and slopped around in the mud for a long time, and finally he ketched a frog, and fetched him in, and give him to this feller, and says:

"Now, if you're ready, set him alongside of Dan'l, with his fore-paws just even with Dan'l, and I'll give the word." Then he says, "One — two — three — jump!" and him and the feller touched up the frogs from behind, and the new frog hopped off, but Dan'l give a heave, and hysted up his shoulders — so — like a Frenchman, but it wan't no use — he couldn't budge; he was planted as solid as an anvil, and he couldn't no more stir than if he was anchored out. Smiley was a good deal surprised, and he was disgusted too, but he didn't have no idea what the matter was, of course.

The feller took the money and started away; and when he was going out at the door, he sorter jerked his thumb over his shoulders — this way — at Dan'l, and says again, very deliberate, "Well, *I* don't see no p'ints about that frog that's any better'n any other frog."

Smiley he stood scratching his head and looking down at Dan'l a long time, and at last he says, "I do wonder what in the nation that frog throw'd off for—I wonder if there an't something the matter with him—he 'pears to look mighty baggy, somehow." And he ketched Dan'l by the nap of the neck, and lifted him up and says, "Why, blame my cats, if he don't weigh five pound!" and turned him upside down, and he belched out a double handful of shot. And then he see how it was, and he was the maddest man—he set the frog down and took out after that feller, but he never ketched him. And—

[Here Simon Wheeler heard his name called from the front yard, and got up to see what was wanted.] And turning to me as he moved away, he said: "Just set where you are, stranger, and rest easy—I an't going to be gone a second."

But, by your leave, I did not think that a continuation of the history of the enterprising vagabond *Jim* Smiley would be likely to afford me much information concerning the Rev. *Leonidas W.* Smiley, and so I started away.

At the door I met the sociable Wheeler returning, and he buttonholed me and recommenced:

"Well, thish-yer Smiley had a yaller one-eyed cow that didn't have no tail, only jest a short stump like a bannanner, and—"

"Oh! hang Smiley and his afflicted cow!"
I muttered, good-naturedly, and bidding the old
gentleman good-day, I departed.

AURELIA'S

UNFORTUNATE YOUNG MAN

Mark Twain

UNFORTUNATE YOUNG MAN

The facts in the following case come to me by letter
from a young lady who lives in the beautiful city
of San José; she is perfectly unknown to me, and
simply signs herself "Aurelia Maria," which may
possibly be a fictitious name. But no matter, the
poor girl is almost heart-broken by the misfortunes
she has undergone, and so confused by the conflicting
counsels of misguided friends and insidious
enemies, that she does not know what course to
pursue in order to extricate herself from the web

17

of difficulties in which she seems almost hopelessly involved. In this dilemma she turns to me for help, and supplicates for my guidance and instruction with a moving eloquence that would touch the heart of a statue. Hear her sad story:

She says that when she was sixteen years old she met and loved, with all the devotion of a passionate nature, a young man from New Jersey, named Williamson Breckinridge Caruthers, who was some six years her senior. They were engaged, with the free consent of their friends and relatives, and for a time it seemed as if their career was destined to be characterized by an immunity from sorrow beyond the usual lot of humanity. But at last the tide of fortune turned; young Caruthers became infected with small-pox of the most virulent type, and when he recovered from his illness, his face was pitted like a waffle-mould and his comeliness gone forever. Aurelia thought to break off the engagement at first, but pity for her unfortunate lover caused her to postpone the marriage-day for a season, and give him another trial.

The very day before the wedding was to have taken place, Breckinridge, while absorbed in watching the flight of a balloon, walked into a well and fractured one of his legs, and it had to be taken off above the knee. Again Aurelia was

moved to break the engagement, but again love
triumphed, and she set the day forward and gave
him another chance to reform.

And again misfortune overtook the unhappy
youth. He lost one arm by the premature discharge
of a Fourth-of-July cannon, and within three
months he got the other pulled out by a carding-
machine. Aurelia's heart was almost crushed by
these latter calamities. She could not but be deeply
grieved to see her lover passing from her by
piecemeal, feeling, as she did, that he could not last
forever under this disastrous process of reduction,
yet knowing of no way to stop its dreadful career,
and in her tearful despair she almost regretted,
like brokers who hold on and lose, that she had
not taken him at first, before he had suffered such an
alarming depreciation. Still, her brave soul bore
her up, and she resolved to bear with her friend's
unnatural disposition yet a little longer.

Again the wedding-day approached, and again
disappointment overshadowed it: Caruthers fell ill
with the erysipelas, and lost the use of one of his
eyes entirely. The friends and relatives of the bride,
considering that she had already put up with more
than could reasonably be expected of her, now came
forward and insisted that the match should be
broken off; but after wavering awhile, Aurelia,

with a generous spirit which did her credit, said she
had reflected calmly upon the matter, and could
not discover that Breckinridge was to blame.

So she extended the time once more, and he broke
his other leg.

It was a sad day for the poor girl when she saw
the surgeons reverently bearing away the sack
whose uses she had learned by previous experience,
and her heart told her the bitter truth that some
more of her lover was gone. She felt that the
field of her affections was growing more and more
circumscribed every day, but once more she frowned
down her relatives and renewed her betrothal.

Shortly before the time set for the nuptials
another disaster occurred. There was but one man
scalped by the Owens River Indians last year.
That man was Williamson Breckinridge Caruthers,
of New Jersey. He was hurrying home with
happiness in his heart, when he lost his hair forever,
and in that hour of bitterness he almost cursed the
mistaken mercy that had spared his head.

At last Aurelia is in serious perplexity as to what
she ought to do. She still loves her Breckinridge,
she writes, with true womanly feeling — she still
loves what is left of him — but her parents are
bitterly opposed to the match, because he has no
property and is disabled from working, and she has

20

not sufficient means to support both comfortably. "Now, what should she do?" she asks with painful and anxious solicitude.

It is a delicate question; it is one which involves the lifelong happiness of a woman, and that of nearly two thirds of a man, and I feel that it would be assuming too great a responsibility to do more than make a mere suggestion in the case. How would it do to build to him? If Aurelia can afford the expense, let her furnish her mutilated lover with wooden arms and wooden legs, and a glass eye and a wig, and give him another show; give him ninety days, without grace, and if he does not break his neck in the mean time, marry him and take the chances. It does not seem to me that there is much risk, any way, Aurelia, because if he sticks to his infernal propensity for damaging himself every time he sees a good opportunity, his next experiment is bound to finish him, and then you are all right, you know, married or single. If married, the wooden legs and such other valuables as he may possess, revert to the widow, and you see you sustain no actual loss save the cherished fragment of a noble but most unfortunate husband, who honestly strove to do right, but whose extraordinary instincts were against him. Try it, Maria! I have thought the matter over carefully and well, and it is the only chance I see for you. It would have been a happy conceit on the part of Caruthers if he had started with his neck and broken that first; but since he has seen fit to choose a different policy and string himself out as long as possible, I do not think we ought to upbraid him for it if he has enjoyed it. We must do the best we can under the circumstances, and try not to feel exasperated at him.

THE STORY OF

THE BAD LITTLE BOY

WHO DIDN'T COME TO GRIEF

Mark Twain

THE STORY OF

THE BAD LITTLE BOY

WHO DIDN'T COME TO GRIEF

Once there was a bad little boy, whose name was Jim — though, if you will notice, you will find that bad little boys are nearly always called James in your Sunday-school books. It was very strange, but still it was true, that this one was called Jim.

He didn't have any sick mother, either — a sick mother who was pious and had the consumption, and would be glad to lie down in the grave and be at rest, but for the strong love she bore her boy, and the anxiety she felt that the world would be

harsh and cold towards him when she was gone.
Most bad boys in the Sunday books are named
James, and have sick mothers, who teach them
to say, "Now I lay me down," etc., and sing them to
sleep with sweet plaintive voices, and then kiss
them good-night, and kneel down by the bedside
and weep. But it was different with this fellow.
He was named Jim, and there wasn't anything the
matter with his mother—no consumption, or
anything of that kind. She was rather stout than
otherwise, and she was not pious; moreover, she was
not anxious on Jim's account. She said if he were
to break his neck, it wouldn't be much loss. She
always spanked Jim to sleep, and she never kissed
him good-night; on the contrary, she boxed his ears
when she was ready to leave him.

Once this little bad boy stole the key of the pantry
and slipped in there and helped himself to some
jam, and filled up the vessel with tar, so that his
mother would never know the difference; but
all at once a terrible feeling didn't come over him,
and something didn't seem to whisper to him,
"Is it right to disobey my mother? Isn't it sinful to
do this? Where do bad little boys go who gobble
up their good kind mother's jam?" and then he
didn't kneel down all alone and promise never
to be wicked any more, and rise up with a light,

26

happy heart, and go and tell his mother all about
it, and beg her forgiveness, and be blessed by her
with tears of pride and thankfulness in her eyes.
No; that is the way with all other bad boys in the
books; but it happened otherwise with this Jim,
strangely enough. He ate that jam, and said it
was bully, in his sinful, vulgar way; and he put in
the tar, and said that was bully also, and laughed,
and observed that "the old woman would get up
and snort" when she found it out; and when she
did find it out, he denied knowing anything about it,
and she whipped him severely, and he did the
crying himself. Every thing about this boy was
curious — every thing turned out differently with
him from the way it does to the bad Jameses
in the books.

Once he climbed up in Farmer Acorn's apple-tree
to steal apples, and the limb didn't break, and he
didn't fall and break his arm, and get torn by the
farmer's great dog, and then languish on a sick
bed for weeks, and repent and become good.
Oh! no; he stole as many apples as he wanted, and
came down all right; and he was all ready for
the dog, too, and knocked him endways with a
rock when he came to tear him. It was very
strange — nothing like it ever happened in those
mild little books with marbled backs, and with

27

pictures in them of men with swallow-tailed coats,
and bell-crowned hats, and pantaloons that are
short in the legs, and women with the waists of their
dresses under their arms and no hoops on.
Nothing like it in any of the Sunday-school books.

Once he stole the teacher's penknife, and when
he was afraid it would be found out, and he would
get whipped, he slipped it into George Wilson's
cap — poor Widow Wilson's son, the moral boy,
the good little boy of the village, who always obeyed
his mother, and never told an untruth, and was
fond of his lessons and infatuated with Sunday-
school. And when the knife dropped from the cap,
and poor George hung his head and blushed, as
if in conscious guilt, and the grieved teacher charged
the theft upon him, and was just in the very act
of bringing the switch down upon his trembling
shoulders, a white-haired improbable justice of the
peace did not suddenly appear in their midst and
strike an attitude and say, "spare this noble boy —
there stands the cowering culprit! I was passing
the school-door at recess, and, unseen myself, I
saw the theft committed!" And then Jim didn't
get whaled, and the venerable justice didn't read the
tearful school a homily, and take George by the
hand and say such a boy deserved to be exalted, and
then tell him to come and make his home with

him, and sweep out the office, and make fires, and
run errands, and chop wood, and study law,
and help his wife to do household labors, and
have all the balance of the time to play, and get
forty cents a month, and be happy. No; it would
have happened that way in the books, but it didn't
happen that way to Jim. No meddling old clam
of a justice dropped in to make trouble, and so
the model boy George got threshed, and Jim was
glad of it; because, you know, Jim hated moral boys.
Jim said he was "down on them milksops." Such
was the coarse language of this bad, neglected
boy.

But the strangest things that ever happened to
Jim was the time he went boating on Sunday and
didn't get drowned, and that other time that he
got caught out in the storm when he was fishing
on Sunday, and didn't get struck by lightning.
Why, you might look, and look, and look through
the Sunday-school books, from now till next
Christmas, and you would never come across
anything like this. Oh! no; you would find that
all the bad boys who go boating on Sunday invariably
get drowned; and all the bad boys who get caught
out in storms, when they are fishing on Sunday,
infallibly get struck by lightning. Boats with
bad boys in them always upset on Sunday, and it

always storms when bad boys go fishing on the Sabbath. How this Jim ever escaped is a mystery to me.

This Jim bore a charmed life—that must have been the way of it. Nothing could hurt him. He even gave the elephant in the menagerie a plug of tobacco, and the elephant didn't knock the top of his head off with his trunk. He browsed around the cupboard after essence of peppermint, and didn't make a mistake and drink aqua fortis. He stole his father's gun and went hunting on the Sabbath, and didn't shoot three or four of his fingers off. He struck his little sister on the temple with his fist when he was angry, and she didn't linger in pain through long summer days, and die with sweet words of forgiveness upon her lips that redoubled the anguish of his breaking heart. No; she got over it. He ran off and went to sea at last, and didn't come back and find himself sad and alone in the world, his loved ones sleeping in the quiet churchyard, and the vine-embowered home of his boyhood tumbled down and gone to decay. Ah! no; he came home drunk as a piper, and got into the station-house the first thing.

And he grew up, and married, and raised a large family, and brained them all with an ax one night, and got wealthy by all manner of cheating and rascality, and now he is the infernalest wickedest scoundrel in his native village, and is universally respected, and belongs to the Legislature.

So you see there never was a bad James in the Sunday-school books that had such a streak of luck as this sinful Jim with the charmed life.

CURING

A COLD

Mark Twain

CURING

A COLD

It is a good thing, perhaps, to write for the amusement
of the public, but it is a far higher and nobler
thing to write for their instruction, their profit, their
actual and tangible benefit. The latter is the
sole object of this article. If it prove the means of
restoring to health one solitary sufferer among
my race, of lighting up once more the fire of
hope and joy in his faded eyes, of bringing back to his
dead heart again the quick, generous impulses of
other days, I shall be amply rewarded for my labor;

my soul will be permeated with the sacred delight
a Christian feels when he has done a good,
unselfish deed.

Having led a pure and blameless life, I am
justified in believing that no man who knows me
will reject the suggestions I am about to make,
out of fear that I am trying to deceive him. Let
the public do itself the honor to read my experience
in doctoring a cold, as herein set forth, and then
follow in my footsteps.

When the White House was burned in Virginia,
I lost my home, my happiness, my constitution,
and my trunk. The loss of the two first-named
articles was a matter of no great consequence, since
a home without a mother or a sister, or a distant
young female relative in it, to remind you, by
putting your soiled linen out of sight and taking
your boots down off the mantle-piece, that there are
those who think about you and care for you, is
easily obtained. And I cared nothing for the loss
of my happiness, because, not being a poet, it
could not be possible that melancholy would abide
with me long.

But to lose a good constitution and a better trunk
were serious misfortunes.

On the day of the fire my constitution succumbed
to a severe cold caused by undue exertion in

36

getting ready to do something. I suffered to no
purpose, too, because the plan I was figuring at
for the extinguishing of the fire was so elaborate that
I never got it completed until the middle of the
following week.

The first time I began to sneeze, a friend told
me to go and bathe my feet in hot water and go
to bed. I did so. Shortly afterward, another friend
advised me to get up and take a cold shower-bath.
I did that also. Within the hour, another friend
assured me that it was policy to "feed a cold and
starve a fever." I had both. So I thought it best to
fill myself up for the cold, and then keep dark
and let the fever starve awhile.

In a case of this kind, I seldom do things by halves;
I ate pretty heartily; I conferred my custom upon
a stranger who had just opened his restaurant
that morning; he waited near me in respectful
silence until I had finished feeding my cold, when he
inquired if the people about Virginia were much
afflicted with colds? I told him I thought they were.
He then went out and took in his sign. I started
down toward the office, and on the way encountered
another bosom friend, who told me that a quart
of salt water, taken warm, would come as near
curing a cold as anything in the world. I hardly
thought I had room for it, but I tried it anyhow.

The result was surprising. I believe I threw up my immortal soul.

Now, as I am giving my experience only for the benefit of those who are troubled with the distemper I am writing about, I feel that they will see the propriety of my cautioning them against following such portions of it as proved inefficient with me, and acting upon this conviction, I warn them against warm salt water. It may be a good enough remedy, but I think it is too severe. If I had another cold in the head, and there were no course left me but to take either an earthquake or a quart of warm salt water, I would take my chances on the earthquake.

After the storm which had been raging in my stomach had subsided, and no more good Samaritans happening along, I went on borrowing handkerchiefs again and blowing them to atoms, as had been my custom in the early stages of my cold, until I came across a lady who had just arrived from over the plains, and who said she had lived in a part of the country where doctors were scarce, and had from necessity acquired considerable skill in the treatment of simple "family complaints." I knew she must have had much experience, for she appeared to be a hundred and fifty years old.

She mixed a decoction composed of molasses,

aqua fortis, turpentine, and various other drugs, and instructed me to take a wine-glass full of it every fifteen minutes. I never took but one dose; that was enough; it robbed me of all moral principle, and awoke every unworthy impulse of my nature. Under its malign influence my brain conceived miracles of meanness, but my hands were too feeble to execute them; at that time, had it not been that my strength had surrendered to a succession of assaults from infallible remedies for my cold, I am satisfied that I would have tried to rob the graveyard.

Like most other people I often feel mean, and act accordingly; but until I took that medicine I had never reveled in such supernatural depravity and felt proud of it. At the end of two days I was ready to go to doctoring again. I took a few more unfailing remedies, and finally drove my cold from my head to my lungs.

I got to coughing incessantly, and my voice fell below zero; I conversed in a thundering base, two octaves below my natural tone; I could only compass my regular nightly repose by coughing myself down to a state of utter exhaustion, and then the moment I began to talk in my sleep, my discordant voice woke me up again.

My case grew more and more serious every day.

Plain gin was recommended; I took it. Then gin
and molasses; I took that also. Then gin and onions;
I added the onions, and took all three. I detected
no particular result, however, except that I had
acquired a breath like a buzzard's.

I found I had to travel for my health. I went to
Lake Bigler with my reportorial comrade, Wilson.
It is gratifying to me to reflect that we traveled
in considerable style; we went in the Pioneer coach,
and my friend took all his baggage with him,
consisting of two excellent silk handkerchiefs and a
daguerreotype of his grandmother. We sailed and
hunted and fished and danced all day, and I
doctored my cough all night. By managing in this
way, I made out to improve every hour in the
twenty-four. But my disease continued to grow
worse.

A sheet-bath was recommended. I had never
refused a remedy yet, and it seemed poor policy to
commence then; therefore I determined to take a
sheet-bath, notwithstanding I had no idea what sort
of arrangement it was.

It was administered at midnight, and the weather
was very frosty. My breast and back were bared,
and a sheet (there appeared to be a thousand yards
of it) soaked in ice-water was wound around
me until I resembled a swab for a Columbiad.

It is a cruel expedient. When the chilly rag touches
one's warm flesh, it makes him start with sudden
violence and gasp for breath just as men do in
the death agony. It froze the marrow in my bones
and stopped the beating of my heart. I thought
my time had come.

Young Wilson said the circumstance reminded
him of an anecdote about a negro who was being
baptized, and who slipped from the parson's grasp,
and came near being drowned. He floundered
around, though, and finally rose up out of the water
considerably strangled and furiously angry, and
started ashore at once, spouting water like a whale,
and remarking, with great asperity, that "One o'
dese days some gen'lman's nigger gwyne to git
killed wid jes' such dam foolishness as dis!"

Never take a sheet-bath—never. Next to meeting
a lady acquaintance, who, for reasons best known
to herself, don't see you when she looks at you,
and don't know you when she does see you, it is the
most uncomfortable thing in the world.

But, as I was saying, when the sheet-bath failed to
cure my cough, a lady friend recommended the
application of a mustard plaster to my breast.
I believe that would have cured me effectually, if it
had not been for young Wilson. When I went to
bed, I put my mustard plaster—which was a very

gorgeous one, eighteen inches square — where I
could reach it when I was ready for it. But young
Wilson got hungry in the night, and ate it up.
I never saw any body have such an appetite; I am
confident that lunatic would have eaten me if I had
been healthy.

After sojourning a week at Lake Bigler, I went to
Steamboat Springs, and beside the steam baths,
I took a lot of the vilest medicines that were ever
concocted. They would have cured me, but I had to
go back to Virginia, where, notwithstanding the
variety of new remedies I absorbed every day,
I managed to aggravate my disease by carelessness
and undue exposure.

I finally concluded to visit San Francisco, and the
first day I got there, a lady at the Lick House told
me to drink a quart of whisky every twenty-four
hours, and a friend at the Occidental recommended
precisely the same course. Each advised me to
take a quart; that made half a gallon. I did it,
and still live.

Now, with the kindest motives in the world, I
offer for the consideration of consumptive patients
the variegated course of treatment I have lately gone
through. Let them try it; if it don't cure them, it
can't more than kill them.

LUCRETIA SMITH'S

SOLDIER

Mark Twain

SOLDIER

I am an ardent admirer of those nice, sickly war stories which have lately been so popular, and for the last three months I have been at work upon one of that character, which is now completed. It can be relied upon as true in every particular, inasmuch as the facts it contains were compiled from the official records in the War Department at Washington. It is but just, also, that I should confess that I have drawn largely on *Jomini's Art of War,* the *Message of the President and Accompanying*

Documents, and sundry maps and military works, so
necessary for reference in building a novel like
this. To the accommodating Directors of the
Overland Telegraph Company I take pleasure in
returning my thanks for tendering me the use of
their wires at the customary rates. And finally, to all
those kind friends who have, by good deeds or
encouraging words, assisted me in my labors upon
this story of "Lucretia Smith's Soldier," during
the past three months, and whose names are too
numerous for special mention, I take this method
of tendering my sincerest gratitude.

CHAPTER I

On a balmy May morning in 1861, the little village
of Bluemass, in Massachusetts, lay wrapped in the
splendor of the newly-risen sun. Reginald de
Whittaker, confidential and only clerk in the house
of Bushrod & Ferguson, general drygoods and
grocery dealers and keepers of the post-office, rose
from his bunk under the counter, and shook himself.
After yawning and stretching comfortably, he
sprinkled the floor and proceeded to sweep it. He had
only half finished his task, however, when he sat
down on a keg of nails and fell into a reverie.
"This is my last day in this shanty," said he. "How
it will surprise Lucretia when she hears I am going

46

for a soldier! How proud she will be, the little
darling!" He pictured himself in all manner of
warlike situations; the hero of a thousand
extraordinary adventures; the man of rising fame;
the pet of Fortune at last; and beheld himself,
finally, returning to his own home, a bronzed and
scarred brigadier-general, to cast his honors and his
matured and perfect love at the feet of his
Lucretia Borgia Smith.

At this point a thrill of joy and pride suffused his
system; but he looked down and saw his broom,
and blushed. He came toppling down from the
clouds he had been soaring among, and was an
obscure clerk again, on a salary of two dollars
and a half a week.

CHAPTER II

At eight o'clock that evening, with a heart
palpitating with the proud news he had brought for
his beloved, Reginald sat in Mr. Smith's parlor
awaiting Lucretia's appearance. The moment she
entered, he sprang to meet her, his face lighted by
the torch of love that was blazing in his head
somewhere and shining through, and ejaculated,
"Mine own!" as he opened his arms to receive her.

"Sir!" said she, and drew herself up like an
offended queen.

Poor Reginald was stricken dumb with astonishment. This chilling demeanor, this angry rebuff, where he had expected the old, tender welcome, banished the gladness from his heart as the cheerful brightness is swept from the landscape when a dark cloud drifts athwart the face of the sun. He stood bewildered a moment, with a sense of goneness on him like one who finds himself suddenly overboard upon a midnight sea, and beholds the ship pass into shrouding gloom, while the dreadful conviction falls upon his soul that he has not been missed. He tried to speak, but his pallid lips refused their office. At last he murmured:

"O Lucretia! what have I done; what is the matter; why this cruel coldness? Don't you love your Reginald any more?"

Her lips curled in bitter scorn, and she replied, in mocking tones:

"Don't I love my Reginald any more? No, I *don't* love my Reginald any more! Go back to your pitiful junk-shop and grab your pitiful yard-stick, and stuff cotton in your ears, so that you can't hear your country shout to you to fall in and shoulder arms. Go!" And then, unheeding the new light that flashed from his eyes, she fled from the room and slammed the door behind her.

Only a moment more! Only a single moment more,

48

he thought, and he could have told her how he had
already answered the summons and signed his name
to the muster-roll, and all would have been well;
his lost bride would have come back to his arms
with words of praise and thanksgiving upon her lips.
He made a step forward, once, to recall her, but
he remembered that he was no longer an effeminate
drygoods student, and his warrior soul scorned to
sue for quarter. He strode from the place with
martial firmness, and never looked behind him.

CHAPTER III

When Lucretia awoke next morning, the faint music
of fife and the roll of a distant drum came floating
upon the soft spring breeze, and as she listened the
sounds grew more subdued, and finally passed out of
hearing. She lay absorbed in thought for many
minutes, and then she sighed and said: "Oh! if he were
only with that band of fellows, how I could love him!"

In the course of the day a neighbor dropped in,
and when the conversation turned upon the soldiers,
the visitor said:

"Reginald de Whittaker looked rather down-
hearted, and didn't shout when he marched along
with the other boys this morning. I expect it's owing
to you, Miss Loo, though when I met him coming
here yesterday evening to tell you he'd enlisted,

he thought you'd like it and be proud of — Mercy!
what in the nation's the matter with the girl?"

Nothing, only a sudden misery had fallen like a
blight upon her heart, and a deadly pallor
telegraphed it to her countenance. She rose up
without a word and walked with a firm step out of
the room; but once within the sacred seclusion of her
own chamber, her strong will gave way and she
burst into a flood of passionate tears. Bitterly she
upbraided herself for her foolish haste of the night
before, and her harsh treatment of her lover at
the very moment that he had come to anticipate the
proudest wish of her heart, and to tell her that he
had enrolled himself under the battle-flag, and
was going forth to fight as *her* soldier. Alas! other
maidens would have soldiers in those glorious fields,
and be entitled to the sweet pain of feeling a tender
solicitude for them, but she would be unrepresented.
No soldier in all the vast armies would breathe her
name as he breasted the crimson tide of war! She
wept again — or, rather, she went on weeping where
she left off a moment before. In her bitterness of
spirit she almost cursed the precipitancy that had
brought all this sorrow upon her young life.
"Drat it!" The words were in her bosom, but she
locked them there, and closed her lips against
their utterance.

For weeks she nursed her grief in silence, while the roses faded from her cheeks. And through it all she clung to the hope that some day the old love would bloom again in Reginald's heart, and he would write to her; but the long summer days dragged wearily along, and still no letter came. The newspapers teemed with stories of battle and carnage, and eagerly she read them, but always with the same result: the tears welled up and blurred the closing lines — the name she sought was looked for in vain, and the dull aching returned to her sinking heart. Letters to the other girls sometimes contained brief mention of him, and presented always the same picture of him — a morose, unsmiling, desperate man, always in the thickest of the fight, begrimed with powder, and moving calm and unscathed through tempest of shot and shell, as if he bore a charmed life.

But at last, in a long list of maimed and killed, poor Lucretia read these terrible words, and fell fainting to the floor: *"R. D. Whittaker, private soldier, desperately wounded!"*

CHAPTER IV

On a couch in one of the wards of a hospital at Washington lay a wounded soldier; his head was so profusely bandaged that his features were not

visible; but there was no mistaking the happy face
of the young girl who sat beside him — it was
Lucretia Borgia Smith's. She had hunted him out
several weeks before, and since that time she had
patiently watched by him and nursed him, coming in
the morning as soon as the surgeon had finished
dressing his wounds, and never leaving him until
relieved at nightfall. A ball had shattered his lower
jaw, and he could not utter a syllable; through all her
weary vigils she had never once been blessed with a
grateful word from his dear lips; yet she stood to her
post bravely and without a murmur, feeling that when
he did get well again she would hear that which
would more than reward her for all her devotion.

At the hour we have chosen for the opening of this
chapter, Lucretia was in a tumult of happy
excitement; for the surgeon had told her that at
last her Whittaker had recovered sufficiently to
admit of the removal of the bandages from his head,
and she was now waiting with feverish impatience
for the doctor to come and disclose the loved
features to her view. At last he came, and Lucretia,
with beaming eyes and fluttering heart, bent over
the couch with anxious expectancy. One bandage
was removed, then another and another, and lo! the
poor wounded face was revealed to the light of day.

"O my own dar—"

What have we here! What is the matter! Alas! it was the face of a stranger!

Poor Lucretia! With one hand covering her upturned eyes, she staggered back with a moan of anguish. Then a spasm of fury distorted her countenance as she brought her fist down with a crash that made the medicine bottles on the table dance again, and exclaimed:

"Oh! confound my cats, if I haven't gone and fooled away three mortal weeks here, snuffling and slobbering over the wrong soldier!"

It was a sad, sad truth. The wretched but innocent and unwitting impostor was R. D., or Richard Dilworthy Whittaker, of Wisconsin, the soldier of dear little Eugenie Le Mulligan, of that State, and utterly unknown to our unhappy Lucretia B. Smith.

Such is life, and the tail of the serpent is over us all. Let us draw the curtain over this melancholy history — for melancholy it must still remain, during a season at least, for the real Reginald de Whittaker has not turned up yet.

AN ITEM WHICH

THE EDITOR HIMSELF

COULD NOT UNDERSTAND

Mark Twain

AN ITEM WHICH

THE EDITOR HIMSELF

COULD NOT UNDERSTAND

Our esteemed friend, Mr. John William Skae, of
Virginia City, walked into the office where we are
sub-editor at a late hour last night, with an
expression of profound and heartfelt suffering upon
his countenance, and, sighing heavily, laid the
following item reverently upon the desk, and walked
slowly out again. He paused a moment at the door,
and seemed struggling to command his feelings
sufficiently to enable him to speak, and then,
nodding his head toward his manuscript, ejaculated

in a broken voice, "Friend of mine — oh! how sad!"
and burst into tears. We were so moved at his
distress that we did not think to call him back and
endeavor to comfort him until he was gone and it
was too late. The paper had already gone to press,
but knowing that our friend would consider the
publication of this item important, and cherishing
the hope that to print it would afford a melancholy
satisfaction to his sorrowing heart, we stopped the
press at once and inserted it in our columns:

DISTRESSING ACCIDENT: Last evening about 6 o'clock,
as Mr. William Schuyler, an old and respectable citizen
of South Park, was leaving his residence to go down
town, as has been his usual custom for many years, with
the exception only of a short interval in the spring of
1850, during which he was confined to his bed by injuries
received in attempting to stop a runaway horse by
thoughtlessly placing himself directly in its wake and
throwing up his hands and shouting, which, if he had
done so even a single moment sooner, must inevitably
have frightened the animal still more instead of checking
its speed, although disastrous enough to himself as it was,
and rendered more melancholy and distressing by reason
of the presence of his wife's mother, who was there and
saw the sad occurrence, notwithstanding it is at least
likely, though not necessarily so, that she should be
reconnoitering in another direction when incidents occur,
not being vivacious and on the lookout, as a general

thing, but even the reverse, as her own mother is said
to have stated, who is no more, but died in the full hope
of a glorious resurrection, upwards of three years ago,
aged 86, being a Christian woman and without guile, as it
were, or property, in consequence of the fire of 1849,
which destroyed every blasted thing she had in the world.
But such is life. Let us all take warning by this solemn
occurrence, and let us endeavor so to conduct ourselves
that when we come to die we can do it. Let us place our
hands upon our hearts, and say with earnestness and
sincerity that from this day forth we will beware of the
intoxicating bowl. *First Edition of the Californian.*

The boss-editor has been in here raising the very
mischief, and tearing his hair and kicking the
furniture about, and abusing me like a pickpocket.
He says that every time he leaves me in charge of
the paper for half an hour, I get imposed upon by
the first infant or the first idiot that comes along.
And he says that distressing item of Johnny Skae's
is nothing but a lot of distressing bosh, and has
got no point to it and no sense in it and no
information in it, and that there was no earthly
necessity for stopping the press to publish it. He says
every man he meets has insinuated that somebody
about *The Californian* office has gone crazy.

Now all this comes of being good-hearted. If I
had been as unaccommodating and unsympathetic
as some people, I would have told Johnny Skae that

I wouldn't receive his communication at such a late hour, and to go to blazes with it; but no, his snuffling distress touched my heart, and I jumped at the chance of doing something to modify his misery. I never read his item to see whether there was any thing wrong about it, but hastily wrote the few lines which preceded it, and sent it to the printers. And what has my kindness done for me? It has done nothing but bring down upon me a storm of abuse and ornamental blasphemy.

Now, I will just read that item myself, and see if there is any foundation for all this fuss. And if there is, the author of it shall hear from me.

I have read it, and I am bound to admit that it seems a little mixed at a first glance. However, I will peruse it once more.

I have read it again, and it does really seem a good deal more mixed than ever.

I have read it over five times, but if I can get at the meaning of it, I wish I may get my just deserts. It won't bear analysis. There are things about it which I can not understand at all. It don't say whatever became of William Schuyler. It just says enough about him to get one interested in his career, and then drops him. Who is William Schuyler, any how, and what part of South Park did he live in, and if he started down-town at six o'clock, did he ever get there, and if he did, did any thing happen to him? Is *he* the individual that met with the "distressing accident"? Considering the elaborate circumstantiality of detail observable in the item, it seems to me that it ought to contain more information than it does. On the contrary, it is obscure — and not only obscure, but utterly incomprehensible. Was the breaking of Mr. Schuyler's leg, fifteen years ago, the "distressing accident" that plunged Mr. Skae into unspeakable grief, and caused him to come up here at dead of night and stop our press to acquaint the world with the unfortunate circumstance? Or did the "distressing accident" consist in the destruction of Schuyler's mother-in-law's property in early times? Or did it consist in the death of that person herself three years ago? (albeit it does not appear that she died by accident.) In a word, what *did* that "distressing accident" consist in? What did that driveling ass of a Schuyler stand *in the wake* of a runaway horse for, with his shouting and gesticulating, if he wanted to stop him? And how the mischief could he get run over by a horse that had already passed beyond him? And what are we to "take warning" by? and how is this extraordinary chapter of incomprehensibilities going to be a "lesson" to us? And above all, what has the "intoxicating bowl" got to do with it, any how? It is not stated that Schuyler drank, or that his wife drank, or that his mother-in-law drank, or that the horse drank—wherefore, then, the reference to the intoxicating bowl? It does seem to me that, if Mr. Skae had let the intoxicating bowl alone himself, he never would have got into so much trouble about this infernal imaginary distressing accident. I have read his absurd item over and over again, with all its insinuating plausibility, until my head swims; but I can make neither head nor tail of it. There certainly seems to have been an accident of some kind or other, but it is impossible to determine what the nature of it was, or who was the sufferer by it. I do not like to do it, but I feel compelled to request that the next time any thing happens to one of Mr. Skae's friends, he will append such explanatory notes to his account of it as will enable me to find out what sort of an accident it was and whom it happened to. I had rather all his friends should die than that I should be driven to the verge of lunacy again in trying to cipher out the meaning of another such production as the above.

A TOUCHING STORY OF

GEORGE WASHINGTON'S

BOYHOOD

Mark Twain

A TOUCHING STORY OF

GEORGE WASHINGTON'S

BOYHOOD

If it please your neighbor to break the sacred calm
of night with the snorting of an unholy trombone, it
is your duty to put up with his wretched music and
your privilege to pity him for the unhappy instinct
that moves him to delight in such discordant sounds.
I did not always think thus: this consideration for
musical amateurs was born of certain disagreeable
personal experiences that once followed the
development of a like instinct in myself. Now this
infidel over the way, who is learning to play on the

trombone, and the slowness of whose progress is
almost miraculous, goes on with his harrowing work
every night, uncursed by me, but tenderly pitied.
Ten years ago, for the same offense, I would have
set fire to his house. At that time I was a prey to an
amateur violinist for two or three weeks, and the
sufferings I endured at his hands are inconceivable.
He played "Old Dan Tucker," and he never played
any thing else; but he performed that so badly that
he could throw me into fits with it if I were awake,
or into a nightmare if I were asleep. As long as he
confined himself to "Dan Tucker," though, I bore
with him and abstained from violence; but when
he projected a fresh outrage, and tried to do "Sweet
Home," I went over and burnt him out. My next
assailant was a wretch who felt a call to play the
clarionet. He only played the scale, however, with
his distressing instrument, and I let him run the
length of his tether, also; but finally, when he
branched out into a ghastly tune, I felt my reason
deserting me under the exquisite torture, and I
sallied forth and burnt him out likewise. During the
next two years I burned out an amateur cornet
player, a bugler, a bassoon-sophomore, and a
barbarian whose talents ran in the base-drum line.

I would certainly have scorched this trombone
man if he had moved into my neighborhood in those

days. But as I said before, I leave him to his own
destruction now, because I have had experience as
an amateur myself, and I feel nothing but
compassion for that kind of people. Besides, I have
learned that there lies dormant in the souls of all
men a penchant for some particular musical
instrument, and an unsuspected yearning to learn
to play on it, that are bound to wake up and demand
attention some day. Therefore, you who rail at
such as disturb your slumbers with unsuccessful and
demoralizing attempts to subjugate a fiddle, beware!
for sooner or later your own time will come. It is
customary and popular to curse these amateurs
when they wrench you out of a pleasant dream at
night with a peculiarly diabolical note; but seeing
that we are all made alike, and must all develop
a distorted talent for music in the fullness of time, it
is not right. I am charitable to my trombone
maniac; in a moment of inspiration he fetches a
snort, sometimes, that brings me to a sitting
posture in bed, broad awake and weltering in a cold
perspiration. Perhaps my first thought is, that there
has been an earthquake; perhaps I hear the
trombone, and my next thought is, that suicide and
the silence of the grave would be a happy release
from this nightly agony; perhaps the old instinct
comes strong upon me to go after my matches; but

my first cool, collected thought is, that the
trombone man's destiny is upon him, and he is
working it out in suffering and tribulation; and I
banish from me the unworthy instinct that would
prompt me to burn him out.

After a long immunity from the dreadful insanity
that moves a man to become a musician in defiance
of the will of God that he should confine himself
to sawing wood, I finally fell a victim to the
instrument they call the accordeon. At this day I
hate that contrivance as fervently as any man can,
but at the time I speak of I suddenly acquired a
disgusting and idolatrous affection for it. I got one of
powerful capacity, and learned to play "Auld Lang
Syne" on it. It seems to me, now, that I must
have been gifted with a sort of inspiration to be
enabled, in the state of ignorance in which I then
was, to select out of the whole range of musical
composition the one solitary tune that sounds vilest
and most distressing on the accordeon. I do not
suppose there is another tune in the world with
which I could have inflicted so much anguish upon
my race as I did with that one during my short
musical career.

After I had been playing "Lang Syne" about a
week, I had the vanity to think I could improve the
original melody, and I set about adding some

little flourishes and variations to it, but with rather indifferent success, I suppose, as it brought my landlady into my presence with an expression about her of being opposed to such desperate enterprises. Said she, "Do you know any other tune but that, Mr. Twain?" I told her, meekly, that I did not. "Well, then," said she, "stick to it just as it is; don't put any variations to it, because it's rough enough on the boarders the way it is now."

The fact is, it was something more than simply "rough enough" on them; it was altogether too rough; half of them left, and the other half would have followed, but Mrs. Jones saved them by discharging me from the premises.

I only staid one night at my next lodging-house. Mrs. Smith was after me early in the morning. She said, "You can go, sir; I don't want you here; I have had one of your kind before — a poor lunatic, that played the banjo and danced breakdowns, and jarred the glass all out of the windows. You kept me awake all night, and if you was to do it again, I'd take and mash that thing over your head!" I could see that this woman took no delight in music, and I moved to Mrs. Brown's.

For three nights in succession I gave my new neighbors "Auld Lang Syne," plain and unadulterated, save by a few discords that rather improved the general effect than otherwise. But the very first time I tried the variations the boarders mutinied. I never did find any body that would stand those variations. I was very well satisfied with my efforts in that house, however, and I left it without any regrets; I drove one boarder as mad as a March hare, and another one tried to scalp his mother. I reflected, though, that if I could only have been allowed to give this latter just one more touch of the variations, he would have finished the old woman.

I went to board at Mrs. Murphy's, an Italian lady of many excellent qualities. The very first time I struck up the variations, a haggard, care-worn, cadaverous old man walked into my room and stood beaming upon me a smile of ineffable happiness. Then he placed his hand upon my head, and looking devoutly aloft, he said with feeling unction, and in a voice trembling with emotion, "God bless you, young man! God bless you! for you have done that for me which is beyond all praise. For years I have suffered from an incurable disease, and knowing my doom was sealed and that I must die, I have striven with all my power to resign myself to my fate, but in vain—the love of life was too strong within me. But Heaven bless you, my benefactor! for since I heard you play that tune and those

variations, I do not want to live any longer —
I am entirely resigned — I am willing to die — in fact,
I am anxious to die." And then the old man fell
upon my neck and wept a flood of happy tears.
I was surprised at these things; but I could not help
feeling a little proud at what I had done, nor could I
help giving the old gentleman a parting blast in
the way of some peculiarly lacerating variations as
he went out at the door. They doubled him up like a
jack-knife, and the next time he left his bed of pain
and suffering he was all right, in a metallic coffin.

My passion for the accordeon finally spent itself
and died out, and I was glad when I found myself
free from its unwholesome influence. While the
fever was upon me, I was a living, breathing
calamity wherever I went, and desolation and
disaster followed in my wake. I bred discord in
families, I crushed the spirits of the light-hearted,
I drove the melancholy to despair, I hurried invalids
to premature dissolution, and I fear me I disturbed
the very dead in their graves. I did incalculable
harm, and inflicted untold suffering upon my race
with my execrable music; and yet to atone for it all,
I did but one single blessed act, in making that
weary old man willing to go to his long home.

Still, I derived some little benefit from that
accordeon; for while I continued to practice on it,

I never had to pay any board—landlords were always willing to compromise, on my leaving before the month was up.

Now, I had two objects in view in writing the foregoing, one of which was to try and reconcile people to those poor unfortunates who feel that they have a genius for music, and who drive their neighbors crazy every night in trying to develop and cultivate it; and the other was to introduce an admirable story about Little George Washington, who could Not Lie, and the Cherry-Tree—or the Apple-Tree—I have forgotten now which, although it was told me only yesterday. And writing such a long and elaborate introductory has caused me to forget the story itself; but it was very touching.

INFORMATION FOR

THE MILLION

INFORMATION FOR

THE MILLION

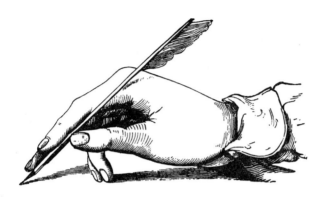

A young man anxious for information writes to a friend residing in Virginia City, Nevada, as follows:

Springfield, Mo., April 12

"Dear Sir: My object in writing to you is to have you give me a full history of Nevada. What is the character of its climate? What are the productions of the earth? Is it healthy? What diseases do they die of mostly? Do you think it would be advisable for a man who can make a living in Missouri to emigrate to that part of the country? There are several of us who would emigrate there in the spring if we could ascertain to a certainty that it is a much better country than this. I suppose you know Joel H. Smith? He used to live here; he lives in Nevada now; they say he owns considerable in a mine there. Hoping to hear from you soon, etc., I remain yours, truly, William ...."

The letter was handed in to a newspaper office for reply. For the benefit of all who contemplate moving to Nevada, it is perhaps best to publish the correspondence in its entirety:

Dearest William: Pardon my familiarity — but that name touchingly reminds me of the loved and lost, whose name was similar. I have taken the contract to answer your letter, and although we are now strangers, I feel we shall cease to be so if we ever become acquainted with each other. The thought is worthy of attention, William. I will now respond to your several propositions in the order in which you have fulminated them.

Your object in writing is to have me give you a full history of Nevada. The flattering confidence you repose in me, William, is only equaled by the modesty of your request. I could detail the history of Nevada in five hundred pages octavo; but as you have never done me any harm, I will spare you, though it will be apparent to every body that I would be justified in taking advantage of

you if I were a mind to. However, I will condense.
Nevada was discovered many years ago by the
Mormons, and was called Carson county. It only
became Nevada in 1861, by act of Congress.
There is a popular tradition that the Almighty
created it; but when you come to see it, William, you
will think differently. Do not let that discourage
you, though. The country looks something like a
singed cat, owing to the scarcity of shrubbery,
and also resembles that animal in the respect that it
has more merits than its personal appearance
would seem to indicate. The Grosch brothers found
the first silver lead here in 1857. They also founded
Silver City, I believe. Signify to your friends,
however, that all the mines here do not pay
dividends as yet; you may make this statement with
the utmost unyielding inflexibility—it will not
be contradicted from this quarter. The population
of this Territory is about 35,000, one half of
which number reside in the united cities of Virginia
and Gold Hill. However, I will discontinue this
history for the present, lest I get you too deeply
interested in this distant land, and cause you to
neglect your family or your religion. But I will
address you again upon the subject next year.
In the mean time, allow me to answer your inquiry
as to the character of our climate.

It has no character to speak of, William, and alas! in this respect it resembles many, ah! too many chambermaids in this wretched, wretched world. Sometimes we have the seasons in their regular order, and then again we have winter all the summer, and summer all winter. Consequently, we have never yet come across an almanac that would just exactly fit this latitude. It is mighty regular about not raining, though, William. It will start in here in November and rain about four, and sometimes as much as seven days on a stretch; after that you may loan out your umbrella for twelve months, with the serene confidence which a Christian feels in four aces. Sometimes the winter begins in November and winds up in June; and sometimes there is a bare suspicion of winter in March and April, and summer all the balance of the year. But as a general thing, William, the climate is good, what there is of it.

What are the productions of the earth? You mean in Nevada, of course. On our ranches here any thing can be raised that can be produced on the fertile fields of Missouri. But ranches are very scattering — as scattering, perhaps, as lawyers in heaven. Nevada, for the most part, is a barren waste of sand, embellished with melancholy sage-brush, and fenced in with snow-clad mountains. But these ghastly features were the salvation of the land,

William; for no rightly constituted American would
have ever come here if the place had been easy of
access, and none of our pioneers would have
staid after they got here, if they had not felt
satisfied that they could not find a smaller chance
for making a living anywhere else. Such is man,
William, as he crops out in America.

"Is it healthy?" Yes, I think it is as healthy here
as it is in any part of the West. But never permit
a question of that kind to vegetate in your brain,
William; because as long as Providence has an eye
on you, you will not be likely to die until your
time comes.

"What diseases do they die of mostly?" Well,
they used to die of conical balls and cold steel,
mostly, but here lately erysipelas and the
intoxicating bowl have got the bulge on those
things, as was very justly remarked by Mr. Rising
last Sunday. I will observe, for your information,
William, that Mr. Rising is our Episcopal minister,
and has done as much as any man among us to
redeem this community from its pristine state of
semi-barbarism. We are afflicted with all the
diseases incident to the same latitude in the States,
I believe, with one or two added and half a dozen
subtracted on account of our superior altitude.
However, the doctors are about as successful here,

both in killing and curing, as they are anywhere.

Now, as to whether it would be advisable for a man who can make a living in Missouri to emigrate to Nevada, I confess I am somewhat mixed. If you are not content in your present condition, it naturally follows that you would be entirely satisfied if you could make either more or less than a living. You would exult in the cheerful exhilaration always produced by a change. Well, you can find your opportunity here, where, if you retain your health, and are sober and industrious, you will inevitably make more than a living, and if you don't, you won't. You can rely upon this statement, William. It contemplates any line of business except the selling of tracts. You can not sell tracts here, William; the people take no interest in tracts; the very best efforts in the tract line — even with pictures on them — have met with no encouragement. Besides, the newspapers have been interfering; a man gets his regular text or so from the Scriptures in his paper, along with the stock sales and the war news, every day now. If you are in the tract business, William, take no chances on Washoe; but you can succeed at any thing else here.

"I suppose you know Joel H. Smith?" Well — the fact is — I believe I don't. Now isn't that singular? Isn't it very singular? And he owns "considerable"

in a mine here too. Happy man! Actually owns in
a mine here in Nevada Territory, and I never
even heard of him. Strange—strange—do you
know, William, it is the strangest thing that ever
happened to me? And then he not only owns in a
mine, but owns "considerable;" that is the strangest
part about it—how a man could own considerable
in a mine in Washoe, and I not know anything
about it. He is a lucky dog, though. But I strongly
suspect that you have made a mistake in the name;
I am confident you have; you mean John Smith—
I know you do; I know it from the fact that he
owns considerable in a mine here, because I sold
him the property at a ruinous sacrifice on the
very day he arrived here from over the plains.
That man will be rich one of these days. I am just
as well satisfied of it as I am of any precisely similar
instance of the kind that has come under my
notice. I said as much to him yesterday, and he
said he was satisfied of it also. But he did not say it
with that air of triumphant exultation which a
heart like mine so delights to behold in one to whom
I have endeavored to be a benefactor in a small
way. He looked pensive awhile, but, finally, says
he, "Do you know, I think I'd a been a rich man
long ago if they'd ever found the d—d ledge?"
That was my idea about it. I always thought, and

I still think, that if they ever do find that ledge,
his chances will be better than they are now. I guess
Smith will be all right one of these centuries, if he
keeps up his assessments—he is a young man yet.
Now, William, I have taken a liking to you, and
I would like to sell you "considerable" in a mine
in Washoe. Let me hear from you on the subject.
Greenbacks at par is as good a thing as I want.
But seriously, William, don't you ever invest in a
mining stock which you don't know any thing about;
beware of John Smith's experience!

You hope to hear from me soon? Very good.
I shall also hope to hear from you soon, about that
little matter above referred to. Now, William,
ponder this epistle well; never mind the sarcasm
here and there, and the nonsense, but reflect upon
the plain facts set forth, because they *are* facts,
and are meant to be so understood and believed.

Remember me affectionately to your friends and
relations, and especially to your venerable
grandmother, with whom I have not the pleasure
to be acquainted—but that is of no consequence,
you know. I have been in your town many a time,
and all the towns of the neighboring counties —
the hotel-keepers will recollect me vividly.
Remember me to them—I bear them no animosity.
Yours affectionately

THE LAUNCH OF

THE STEAMER CAPITAL

Mark Twain

THE STEAMER CAPITAL

I get Mr. Muff Nickerson to go with me and assist
in reporting the great steamboat launch. — He relates the
interesting history of the traveling panoramist.

I was just starting off to see the launch of the great
steamboat Capital, on Saturday week, when I
came across Mulph, Mulff, Muff, Mumph, Murph,
Mumf, Murf, Mumford, Mulford, Murphy
Nickerson — (he is well known to the public by all

these names, and I can not say which is the right
one) — bound on the same errand.

This was the man I wanted.

We set out in a steamer whose decks were
crowded with persons of all ages, who were happy in
their nervous anxiety to behold the novelty of
a steamboat launch.

As we approached the spot where the launch was
to take place, a gentleman from Reese River, by
the name of Thompson, came up, with several
friends, and said he had been prospecting on the
main deck, and had found an object of interest —
a bar. This was all very well, and showed him to be
a man of parts; but like many another man who
produces a favorable impression by an introductory
remark replete with wisdom, he followed it up
with a vain and unnecessary question — Would
we take a drink? This to me! — This to M. M. M.,
etc., Nickerson!

We proceeded, two by two, arm-in-arm, down to
the bar in the nether regions, chatting pleasantly
and elbowing the restless multitude. We took pure,
cold, health-giving water, with some other things
in it, and clinked our glasses together, and
were about to drink, when Smith, of Excelsior, drew
forth his handkerchief and wiped away a tear;
and then, noticing that the action had excited some

attention, he explained it by recounting a most
affecting incident in the history of a venerated aunt
of his — now deceased — and said that, although
long years had passed since the touching event
he had narrated, he could never take a drink without
thinking of the kind-hearted old lady.

Mr. Nickerson blew his nose, and said with deep
emotion that it gave him a better opinion of
human nature to see a man who had had a good
aunt, eternally and forever thinking about her.

This episode reminded Jones, of Mud Springs, of a
circumstance which happened many years ago in
the home of his childhood, and we held our glasses
untouched and rested our elbows on the counter,
while we listened with rapt attention to his story.

There was something in it about a good-natured,
stupid man, and this reminded Thompson, of
Reese River, of a person of the same kind whom
he had once fallen in with while traveling through
the back settlements of one of the Atlantic States,
and we postponed drinking until he should give
us the facts in the case. The hero of the tale had
unintentionally created some consternation at a
camp-meeting by one of his innocent asinine freaks;
and this reminded Mr. M. Nickerson of a
reminiscence of his temporary sojourn in the interior
of Connecticut some months ago; and again our

uplifted glasses were staid on their way to our lips, and we listened attentively to

The entertaining history of the scriptural panoramist.

[I give the history in Mr. Nickerson's own language.]

There was a fellow traveling around, in that country, (said Mr. Nickerson,) with a moral religious show — a sort of a scriptural panorama — and he hired a wooden-headed old slab to play the piano for him. After the first night's performance, the showman says:

"My friend, you seem to know pretty much all the tunes there are, and you worry along first-rate. But then didn't you notice that sometimes last night the piece you happened to be playing was a little rough on the proprieties, so to speak — didn't seem to jibe with the general gait of the picture that was passing at the time, as it were — was a little foreign to the subject, you know — as if you didn't either trump or follow suit, you understand?"

"Well, no," the fellow said; he hadn't noticed, but it might be; he had played along just as it came handy.

So they put it up that the simple old dummy was to keep his eye on the panorama after that, and

as soon as a stunning picture was reeled out, he
was to fit it to a dot with a piece of music that
would help the audience get the idea of the subject,
and warm them up like a camp-meeting revival.
That sort of thing would corral their sympathies,
the showman said.

There was a big audience that night — mostly
middle-aged and old people who belonged to the
church and took a strong interest in Bible matters,
and the balance were pretty much young bucks
and heifers — *they* always come out strong on
panoramas, you know, because it gives them a
chance to taste one another's mugs in the dark.

Well, the showman began to swell himself up for
his lecture, and the old mud-dobber tackled the
piano and run his fingers up and down once or twice
to see that she was all right, and the fellows
behind the curtain commenced to grind out the
panorama. The showman balanced his weight on his
right foot, and propped his hands on his hips,
and flung his eye over his shoulder at the scenery,
and says:

"Ladies and gentlemen, the painting now before
you illustrates the beautiful and touching parable
of the Prodigal Son. Observe the happy expression
just breaking over the features of the poor suffering
youth — so worn and weary with his long march;

note also the ecstasy beaming from the uplifted
countenance of the aged father, and the joy that
sparkles in the eyes of the excited group of youths
and maidens, and seems ready to burst in a
welcoming chorus from their lips. The lesson, my
friends, is as solemn and instructive as the story
is tender and beautiful."

The mud-dobber was all ready, and the second
the speech was finished he struck up:

"Oh! we'll all get blind drunk
  When Johnny comes marching home!"

Some of the people giggled, and some groaned a
little. The showman couldn't say a word. He looked
at the piano-sharp; but he was all lovely and
serene — *he* didn't know there was any thing
out of gear.

The panorama moved on, and the showman
drummed up his grit and started in fresh:

"Ladies and gentlemen, the fine picture now
unfolding itself to your gaze exhibits one of the most
notable events in Bible history — our Saviour
and his disciples upon the Sea of Galilee. How
grand, how awe-inspiring are the reflections which
the subject invokes! What sublimity of faith is
revealed to us in this lesson from the sacred writings!

The Saviour rebukes the angry waves, and walks
securely upon the bosom of the deep!"

All around the house they were whispering,
"Oh! how lovely! how beautiful!" and the orchestra
let himself out again:

"Oh! a life on the ocean wave,
  And a home on the rolling deep!"

There was a good deal of honest snickering turned on
this time, and considerable groaning, and one or
two old deacons got up and went out. The showman
gritted his teeth and cursed the piano man to
himself; but the fellow sat there like a knot on a log,
and seemed to think he was doing first-rate.

After things got quiet, the showman thought he
would make one more stagger at it, any how, though
his confidence was beginning to get mighty shaky.
The supes started the panorama to grinding along
again, and he says:

"Ladies and gentlemen, this exquisite painting
illustrates the raising of Lazarus from the dead
by our Saviour. The subject has been handled with
rare ability by the artist, and such touching
sweetness and tenderness of expression has he thrown
into it, that I have known peculiarly sensitive
persons to be even affected to tears by looking at it.

Observe the half-confused, half-inquiring look,
upon the countenance of the awakening Lazarus.
Observe, also, the attitude and expression of the
Saviour, who takes him gently by the sleeve of his
shroud with one hand, while he points with the
other toward the distant city."

Before any body could get off an opinion in the
case, the innocent old ass at the piano struck up:

"Come, rise up, William Ri-i-ley
 And go along with me!"

It was rough on the audience, you bet you. All the
solemn old flats got up in a huff to go, and every
body else laughed till the windows rattled.

The showman went down and grabbed the
orchestra, and shook him up, and says:

"That lets you out, you know, you chowder-
headed old clam! Go to the doorkeeper and get
your money, and cut your stick! vamose the ranche!
Ladies and gentlemen, circumstances over which
I have no control compel me prematurely to
dismiss — "

"By George! it was splendid! Come! all hands!
let's take a drink!"

It was Phelim O'Flannigan, of San Luis Obispo,
who interrupted. I had not seen him before.

92

"What was splendid?" I inquired.

"The launch!"

Our party clinked glasses once more, and drank in respectful silence.

P. S.: You will excuse me from making a model report of the great launch. I was with Mulf Nickerson, who was going to "explain the whole thing to me as clear as glass;" but, you see, they launched the boat with such indecent haste, that we never got a chance to see it. It was a great pity, because Mulph Nickerson understands launches as well as any man.

CONCERNING

CHAMBERMAIDS

Mark Twain

CHAMBERMAIDS

Against all chambermaids, of whatsoever age or nationality, I launch the curse of bachelordom!

Because:

They always put the pillows at the opposite end of the bed from the gas-burner, so that while you read and smoke before sleeping, (as is the ancient and honored custom of bachelors,) you have to hold your book aloft, in an uncomfortable position, to keep the light from dazzling your eyes.

When they find the pillows removed to the other end of the bed in the morning, they receive not

the suggestion in a friendly spirit; but, glorying
in their absolute sovereignty, and unpitying your
helplessness, they make the bed just as it was
originally, and gloat in secret over the pang their
tyranny will cause you.

Always after that, when they find you have
transposed the pillows, they undo your work, and
thus defy and seek to embitter the life that God
has given you.

If they can not get the light in an inconvenient
position any other way, they move the bed.

If you pull your trunk out six inches from the
wall, so that the lid will stay up when you open it,
they always shove that trunk back again. They
do it on purpose.

If you want the spittoon in a certain spot, where
it will be handy, they don't, and so they move it.

They always put your other boots into
inaccessible places. They chiefly enjoy depositing
them as far under the bed as the wall will permit.
It is because this compels you to get down in an
undignified attitude and make wild sweeps for
them in the dark with the boot-jack, and swear.

They always put the match-box in some other
place. They hunt up a new place for it every day,
and put up a bottle, or other perishable glass
thing, where the box stood before. This is to cause

you to break that glass thing, groping in the dark,
and get yourself into trouble.

They are forever and ever moving the furniture.
When you come in, in the night, you can calculate
on finding the bureau where the wardrobe was
in the morning. And when you go out in the
morning, if you leave the slop-bucket by the door
and rocking-chair by the window, when you
come in at midnight, or thereabouts, you will fall
over that rocking-chair, and you will proceed
toward the window and sit down in that slop-tub.
This will disgust you. They like that.

No matter where you put any thing, they are not
going to let it stay there. They will take it and move it
the first chance they get. It is their nature. And,
besides, it gives them pleasure to be mean and contrary
this way. They would die if they couldn't be villains.

They always save up all the old scraps of printed
rubbish you throw on the floor, and stack them up
carefully on the table, and start the fire with
your valuable manuscripts. If there is any one
particular old scrap that you are more down on
than any other, and which you are gradually
wearing your life out trying to get rid of, you may
take all the pains you possibly can in that direction,
but it won't be of any use, because they will
always fetch that old scrap back and put it in the

same old place again every time. It does them good.

And they use up more hair-oil than any six men.
If charged with purloining the same, they lie about
it. What do they care about a hereafter?
Absolutely nothing.

If you leave your key in the door for convenience
sake, they will carry it down to the office and give
it to the clerk. They do this under the vile pretense
of trying to protect your property from thieves;
but actually they do it because they want to make
you tramp back down-stairs after it when you
come home tired, or put you to the trouble of
sending a waiter for it, which waiter will expect
you to pay him something. In which case I suppose
the degraded creatures divide.

They keep always trying to make your bed before
you get up, thus destroying your rest and inflicting
agony upon you; but after you get up, they don't
come any more till next day.

They do all the mean things they can think of,
and they do them just out of pure cussedness,
and nothing else.

Chambermaids are dead to every human instinct.

I have cursed them in behalf of outraged
bachelordom. They deserve it. If I can get a bill
through the Legislature abolishing chambermaids,
I mean to do it.

REMARKABLE INSTANCES OF

PRESENCE OF MIND

Mark Twain

PRESENCE OF MIND

The steamer Ajax encountered a terrible storm on
her down trip from San Francisco to the Sandwich
Islands. It tore her light spars and rigging all to
shreds and splinters, upset all furniture that could
be upset, and spilled passengers around and knocked
them hither and thither with a perfect looseness.
For forty-eight hours no table could be set, and
every body had to eat as best they might under
the circumstances. Most of the party went hungry,
though, and attended to their praying. But there

was one set of "seven-up" players who nailed a
card-table to the floor and stuck to their game
through thick and thin. Captain F...., of a great
banking-house in San Francisco, a man of great
coolness and presence of mind, was of this party.
One night the storm suddenly culminated in a
climax of unparalleled fury; the vessel went down
on her beam ends, and every thing let go with a
crash — passengers, tables, cards, bottles —
every thing came clattering to the floor in a chaos
of disorder and confusion. In a moment fifty sore
distressed and pleading voices ejaculated,
"O Heaven! help us in our extremity!" and one
voice rang out clear and sharp above the plaintive
chorus and said, "Remember, boys, I played the
tray for low!" It was one of the gentlemen I have
mentioned who spoke. And the remark showed
good presence of mind and an eye to business.

Lewis L...., of a great hotel in San Francisco, was
a passenger. There were some savage grizzly bears
chained in cages on deck. One night, in the midst
of a hurricane, which was accompanied by rain
and thunder and lightning, Mr. L. came up, on his
way to bed. Just as he stepped into the pitchy
darkness of the deck and reeled to the still more
pitchy motion of the vessel, (bad,) the captain sang
out hoarsely through his speaking-trumpet,

"Bear a hand aft, there!" The words were sadly
marred and jumbled by the roaring wind. Mr. L....
thought the captain said, "The bears are after you
there!" and he "let go all holts" and went down
into his boots. He murmured, "I knew how it was
going to be — I just knew it from the start — I said
all along that those bears would get loose some time;
and now I'll be the first man that they'll snatch.
Captain! captain! — can't hear me — storm roars
so! O God! what a fate! I have avoided wild beasts
all my life, and now to be eaten by a grizzly bear
in the middle of the ocean, a thousand miles from
land! Captain! O captain! — bless my soul, there's
one of them — I've got to cut and run!" And he
did cut and run, and smashed through the door
of the first state-room he came to. A gentleman and
his wife were in it. The gentleman exclaimed,
"Who's that?" The refugee gasped out, "O great
Scotland! those bears are loose, and just raising
merry hell all over the ship!" and then sank down
exhausted. The gentleman sprang out of bed and
locked the door, and prepared for a siege. After
a while, no assault being made, a reconnaissance
was made from the window, and a vivid flash of
lightning revealed a clear deck. Mr. L.... then made
a dart for his own state-room, gained it, locked
himself in, and felt that his body's salvation was

accomplished, and by little less than a miracle.
The next day the subject of this memoir, though
still very feeble and nervous, had the hardihood to
make a joke upon his adventure. He said that when
he found himself in so tight a place (as he thought)
he didn't bear it with much fortitude, and when he
found himself safe at last in his state-room, he
regarded it as the bearest escape he had ever had in
his life. He then went to bed, and did not get
up again for nine days. This unquestionably bad
joke cast a gloom over the whole ship's company,
and no effort was sufficient to restore their wonted
cheerfulness until the vessel reached her port,
and other scenes erased it from their memories.

HONORED AS

A CURIOSITY

IN HONOLULU

Mark Twain

A CURIOSITY

IN HONOLULU

If you get into conversation with a stranger in
Honolulu, and experience that natural desire to
know what sort of ground you are treading on by
finding out what manner of man your stranger is,
strike out boldly and address him as "Captain."
Watch him narrowly, and if you see by his
countenance that you are on the wrong track,
ask him where he preaches. It is a safe bet that he is
either a missionary or captain of a whaler.
I became personally acquainted with seventy-two

captains and ninety-six missionaries. The captains
and ministers form one half of the population; the
third fourth is composed of common Kanakas and
mercantile foreigners and their families; and the
final fourth is made up of high officers of the
Hawaiian government. And there are just about cats
enough for three apiece all around.

A solemn stranger met me in the suburbs one day,
and said:

"Good morning, your reverence. Preach in the
stone church yonder, no doubt?"

"No, I don't. I'm not a preacher."

"Really, I beg your pardon, captain. I trust you
had a good season. How much oil—"

"Oil! Why, what do you take me for? I'm not a
whaler."

"Oh! I beg a thousand pardons, your Excellency.
Major-General in the household troops, no doubt?
Minister of the Interior, likely? Secretary of War?
First Gentleman of the Bed-chamber? Commissioner
of the Royal—"

"Stuff! man. I'm no official. I'm not connected
in any way with the government."

"Bless my life! Then who the mischief are you?
what the mischief are you? and how the
mischief did you get here? and where in thunder
did you come from?"

"I'm only a private personage — an unassuming
stranger — lately arrived from America."

"No! Not a missionary! not a whaler! not a
member of his Majesty's government! not even
Secretary of the Navy! Ah! heaven! it is too blissful
to be true; alas! I do but dream. And yet that
noble, honest countenance — those oblique,
ingenuous eyes — that massive head, incapable
of — of — anything; your hand; give me your hand,
bright waif. Excuse these tears. For sixteen weary
years I have yearned for a moment like this,
and — "

Here his feelings were too much for him, and he
swooned away. I pitied this poor creature from
the bottom of my heart. I was deeply moved. I shed
a few tears on him, and kissed him for his mother.
I then took what small change he had, and
"shoved."

SHORT AND

SINGULAR RATIONS

Mark Twain

SINGULAR RATIONS

As many will remember, the clipper-ship Hornet, of
New York, was burned at sea on her passage to
San Francisco. The disaster occurred in lat. 2° 20′
north, long. 112° 8′ west. After being forty-three
days adrift on the broad Pacific, in open boats, the
crew and passengers succeeded in making Hawaii.
A tribute to the courage and brave endurance of
these men has been paid in a letter detailing their
sufferings, (the particulars being gathered from their
own lips,) from which the following excerpt is made:

115

On Monday, the thirty-eighth day after the
disaster, "we had nothing left," said the third mate,
"but a pound and a half of ham—the bone was a
good deal the heaviest part of it—and one
soup-and-bully tin." These things were divided
among the fifteen men, and they ate it all—two
ounces of food to each man. I do not count the
ham-bone, as that was saved for next day. For some
time, now, the poor wretches had been cutting their
old boots into small pieces and eating them. They
would also pound wet rags to a sort of pulp and
eat them.

On the thirty-ninth day the ham-bone was divided
up into rations, and scraped with knives and eaten.
I said, "You say the two sick men remained sick
all through, and after a while two or three had
to be relieved from standing watch; how did you get
along without medicines?"

The reply was, "Oh! we couldn't have kept them
if we'd had them; if we'd had boxes of pills, or
any thing like that, we'd have eaten them. It was
just as well—we couldn't have kept them, and we
couldn't have given them to the sick men alone—
we'd have shared them around all alike, I guess."
It was said rather in jest, but it was a pretty true
jest, no doubt.

After apportioning the ham-bone, the captain cut

the canvas cover that had been around the ham
into fifteen equal pieces, and each man took his
portion. This was the last division of food the
captain made. The men broke up the small oaken
butter tub, and divided the staves among
themselves, and gnawed them up. The shell of a
little green turtle was scraped with knives, and eaten
to the last shaving. The third mate chewed pieces
of boots, and spit them out, but ate nothing except
the soft straps of two pairs of boots — ate three
on the thirty-ninth day, and saved one for the
fortieth.

The men seem to have thought in their own minds
of the shipwrecked mariner's last dreadful
resort — cannibalism; but they do not appear to
have conversed about it. They only thought of the
casting lots and killing one of their number as a
possibility; but even when they were eating rags,
and bone, and boots, and shell, and hard oak wood,
they seem to have still had a notion that it was
remote. They felt that some one of the company
must die soon — which one they well knew; and
during the last three or four days of their terrible
voyage they were patiently but hungrily waiting
for him. I wonder if the subject of these anticipations
knew what they were thinking of? He must have
known it — he must have felt it. They had even

calculated how long he would last. They said
to themselves, but not to each other — I think they
said, "He will die Saturday — and then!"

There was one exception to the spirit of delicacy I
have mentioned — a Frenchman — who kept an
eye of strong personal interest upon the sinking
man, and noted his failing strength with untiring
care and some degree of cheerfulness. He frequently
said to Thomas, "I think he will go off pretty soon
now, sir; and then we'll eat him!" This is very sad.

Thomas, and also several of the men, state that
the sick "Portyghee," during the five days that
they were entirely out of provisions, actually ate
two silk handkerchiefs and a couple of cotton shirts,
besides his share of the boots, and bones, and
lumber.

Captain Mitchell was fifty-six years old on the
twelfth of June — the fortieth day after the burning
of the ship and the third day before the boat's
crew reached land. He said it looked somewhat as
if it might be the last one he was going to enjoy.
He had no birthday feast except some bits of
ham-canvas — no luxury but this, and no substantials
save the leather and oaken bucket-staves.

Speaking of the leather diet, one of the men told
me he was obliged to eat a pair of boots which were
so old and rotten that they were full of holes; and

then he smiled gently and said he didn't know,
though, but what the holes tasted about as good
as the balance of the boot. This man was
very feeble, and after saying this he went to bed.

This edition of

THE CELEBRATED JUMPING FROG

OF CALAVERAS COUNTY

AND OTHER SKETCHES

is published by
West Virginia Pulp and Paper Company.

It is designed by
Bradbury Thompson
with reference made to the format
of the first edition published in 1867.

The type faces are
Monotype Modern Number Eight and
Haas Clarendon Bold.

The text pages are printed by letterpress on
Pinnacle Offset, Cream White;
the end sheets are printed by offset lithography on
Clear Spring Buff Envelope Kraft.

The cover is
Clear Spring Buff Envelope Kraft,
and cowhide leather,
with titles stamped in gold.

The slip case is
Clear Spring Buff Envelope Kraft.

All wood engravings are from
Book of Specimens,
MacKellar, Smiths & Jordans,
except the portrait and frog which are from
The Bettmann Archive.

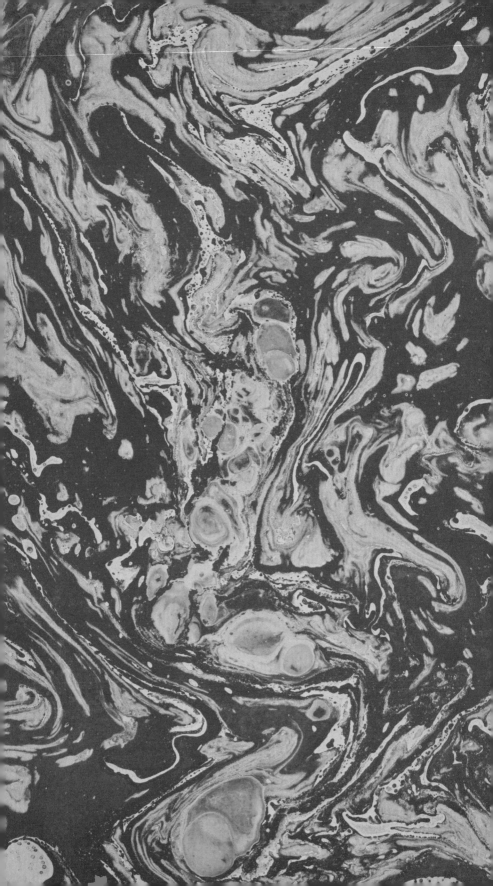